Snozz

Gargoyle

Snorky

Gumph

Jarred

crab

Nessie

Matilda

Eyeball

Sloppy

Trog   # Hairy

Medusa

Hag

Bull

Snout

Rough

Troll-In-The-Box

Batty

Snurkle

Mertle

Spider

Shaggy

Wavy

Pet

Vampire

Rah

Blob

Dev   Rock

Slimey

Slug

Flokk

Gumble

Warty

Dragon

Ted

Smelly

colly

Nun

Sharky

Larry

Potty

Verm

Horn

Tree

Mad Monster

Mummy

Big one

Bendy

Eavesdrop

Squabble

Skull

Snail

Rambo

frankenstein

cyclops

Glum

Scary

Witch

Jagged

Aaargh!

Troll

Bert

Hal

Nerd

cloaked Monster

Squat

Werewolf

Robot

Lippy

Merlin

Granny

Grandad

Fingers

Pumpkin

Spot

Dalek

Baby

Happy

Growl

Wingding

Google

Johnny

Exterminate

Vanilla

Hattie

Bulldog

Venus flytrap

Slurp

Horned Beast

Big Mouth

Snorkel

Helmet

Herm

Beaky

Woo

Slump

Goggle Eyes

Truck

Slime